SONGS OF FELLOWSHIP

Songs of Fellowship

for praise and worship

KINGSWAY PUBLICATIONS

EASTBOURNE

First published 1981
Reprinted 1981
Reprinted 1982

ISBNs 0 86065 117 7 (music wire-o)
0 86065 160 6 (music cased)
0 86065 191 6 (music loose-leaf)
0 86065 118 5 (words)

The publishers wish to thank arranger Margaret Evans
for her work in the preparation of this volume.

Note on the order of songs

The songs appear in alphabetical order by first
line, not necessarily by author's title, for easy
use in praise and worship meetings. An index of
titles and first lines is included at the back.

Printed in Great Britain for
KINGSWAY PUBLICATIONS LTD
Lottbridge Drove, Eastbourne, E. Sussex BN23 6NT by
Richard Clay (The Chaucer Press) Ltd, Bungay, Suffolk.

1.

Abba Father

Capo 3 (G)

D. Bilbrough

Thoughtfully

Ab - ba Fa - ther, let me be Yours and Yours a -
lone. May my will for - e - ver be
Ev - er more Your own. Ne - ver let my heart grow
cold, Ne - ver let me go, Ab - ba
Fa - ther, let me be Yours and Yours a - lone.

2.

Ascribe to the Lord

Caroline Govier

2.   The voice of the Lord is upon the waters,
     Full of majesty.
     His voice thunders through the clouds,
     His temple cries, 'Glory!'

3.   The Lord is enthroned as King for ever,
     Triumph is given to Him.
     Victory He shares with His anointed,
     Earth belongs to Him.

3. Ask and it shall be given

A. Woodroffe/C. Head

pray in the name of God's Son. ____

____ God has placed with -

in our ____ hearts ____ A know - ledge ____ of

His ____ per - fect will, ____ And

4.

As the sun is high

P. Lawson-Johnston

Smoothly

As the sun is high _____ so is my love up-
on _____ you, _____ As the rain ___ falls _____ so will my
love ___ flow. _____ As the rain - bow _____ my pro-mise for
ev - er _____ is true love a-mong ___ you, _____ So let my
love _____ flow _____ from your heart. _____

5. Being myself in the Lord

Gerald Coates/Mick Ray

6. Bind us together

B. Gillman

Verse

1. There is on-ly one God.

There is on-ly one King.

There is on-ly one Bo-dy.

D.C. al Fine

That is why we sing.

2. Made for the glory of God,
   Purchased by His precious Son.
   Born with the right to be clean,
   For Jesus the victory has won. . . .

3. You are the family of God.
   You are the promise divine.
   You are God's chosen desire.
   You are the glorious new wine. . . .

7. Blessed are the pure in heart

2. To see God, the everlasting Father.
   To see God, whose love endures for ever.
   To see God, how wonderful to think that this could be.

3. To see God, the God who talked with Moses.
   To see God, whose mercies are so endless.
   To see God, what better incentive for purity.

4. To see God, the One I've loved and longed for.
   To see God, the Father of my Saviour.
   To see God, a dream come true, at last His face I'll see.

8. Break forth and sing for joy

Joyfully

Paul Armstrong

9. Break forth into joy, O my soul

author unknown
arranged Margaret Evans

Brightly

Break forth in-to joy, O my soul, _____ Break forth in-to joy, O my soul. In the

pres-ence of the Lord there is joy for ev-er-more, Break forth, break forth in-to joy. _____

10.

But ye are washed

P. Simmons

Worshipfully

But ye are washed, _____ But ye are sanc - ti - fied; But ye are jus - ti - fied _____ in the name _____ of the Lord Je - sus, of the Lord Je - sus, And by the Spi - rit of _____ our God.

11.

Cause me to come

R. Edward Miller

Capo 2 (C)

Thoughtfully

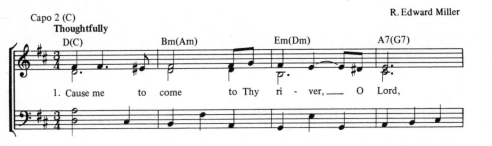

1. Cause me to come to Thy ri - ver, ___ O Lord,

Cause me to come to Thy ri - ver, ___ O Lord,

Cause me to come to Thy ri - ver, ___ O Lord, Cause me to

come, Cause me to drink, Cause me to live.

2. Cause me to drink from Thy river, O Lord, *(three times)*
   Cause me to come, cause me to drink, cause me to live.

3. Cause me to live by Thy river, O Lord, *(three times)*
   Cause me to come, cause me to drink, cause me to live.

12. City, O City

Capo 3(C)

L.E. Smith Jnr.

Brightly with pace

glor- i - ous things are spo-ken __ of you. __

Popular Version

2. This one and that one were born in her,
   All my springs of joy are in You.   *(repeat)*
      Yes all my springs of joy are in You:
   This one and that one were born in her,
   All my springs of joy are in You.

3. Singers and dancers together say,
   'All our springs of joy are in You.' *(repeat)*
      Yes, all our springs of joy are in You:
   Singers and dancers together say,
   'All our springs of joy are in You.'

Original Version

2. More than every other dwelling place
   The Lord loves Zion's gates.   *(repeat)*
      How the Lord loves
      The gates of Zion.
   More than every other dwelling place
   The Lord loves Zion's gates.

3. This one and that one were born in her,
   The Most High will establish her.   *(repeat)*
      About Zion
      It shall be said:
   This one and that one were born in her,
   The Most High will establish her.

4. The Lord will count when He registers
   All the people born in Zion.
   The Lord will count when He registers:
   This one was born in her.
      Then those who sing
      And those who play the flute shall say to Him:
   All of my springs of joy are in You,
   All my springs of joy are in You.

13. Come, all you thirsty nations
(Love is waiting here)

P. Lawson-Johnston

Liltingly

1. Come, all you thir - sty na - tions,___ Come to the ri - ver side.___ If your foun-tains have run dry then come and be sa - tis - fied.___

life ___

e - ver - last - ing life, ___ e - ver - last - ing

life, ___ e - ver - last - ing life. ___

2. How many sons in glory
   Only the Father knows;
   How many will be touched with love
   As the wind of the Spirit blows.

   How many have found freedom,
   How many have found joy,
   Knowing the love that comes from Jesus
   Nothing can destroy,
   Nothing can destroy.

   Come through to Jesus,
   The Lord is waiting for you.
   Come through to Jesus,
   The water is so clear,
   Love is waiting here
   A stream of everlasting life,
   Everlasting life, everlasting life.

14. Come and praise Him, royal priesthood

15. Come bless the Lord

P. Lawson-Johnston

Come bless the Lord, _____ All you ser-vants of the Lord, _____ Who stand by night in the house of the Lord. _____ Lift up your hands _____ to the ho-ly place and bless _____ the _ Lord. _____ Come bless the Lord, _____ Come bless the Lord, _____ Come bless the Lord.

16.   Come bless the Lord

ALTERNATIVE VERSION
arranged Margaret Evans

17.   Come, walk with me

P. Ive

Lightly with pace

1. Come, walk with me round the walls of the ci - ty, See what the King has been build-ing so well. Put down your tools rest a - while from your la - bours, Lift up your eyes, lift your hands, come and see. Come, dance with me round the walls of the ci - ty, Let us give glo - ry to Je - sus our King.

2. You are the stones, which His love is now shaping,
    Lives being made into praise for our God,
    See the pure stone that the builders rejected
    Now the foundation, the glory of God.
    Come dance with me, we're the stones of that city,
    Giving the glory to Jesus our King.

18. Cover me

R. Edward Miller

Tenderly

Cov-er me, _____ cov-er me, _____ ex-tend the bor-der of Thy man-tle ov-er me, Be-cause Thou art _____ my near-est kins-man, _____ Co-ver me, co-ver me, co-ver me. _____

19. Delight yourselves in the Lord

Dave Bolton

Brightly

De - light your-selves in the Lord, _____ de - light your-selves in the Lord, _____ for He de - lights in the prai - ses of His own peo - ple, _____ for He de - lights in the prai - ses of His own peo - ple. Let your well spring up with - in and o - ver-flow to one an - o - ther, let your well spring up with - in and o - ver-flow to the Lord. _____

20.   Draw near to God

Unhurried   Achor

Draw near to God and He'll draw near to you,

Draw near to God and He'll draw near to you.

Last Time He'll draw near to you. *Fine* Lift up ho-ly

hands to Him and sing of what He's done, Op-en up your

hearts to Him and praise Him for His Son. *D.C.*

21. Father, I place into Your hands

Capo 1 (E)

Gently

J. Hewer

2. Father, I place into Your hands
My friends and family.
Father, I place into Your hands
The things that trouble me.
Father, I place into Your hands
The person I would be,
For I know I always can trust You.

3. Father, we love to see Your face,
We love to hear Your voice,
Father, we love to sing your praises
And in Your name rejoice,
Father, we love to walk with You
And in Your presence rest,
For we know we always can trust You.

4. Father, I want to be with You
And do the things You do.
Father, I want to speak the words
That You are speaking too.
Father, I want to love the ones
That You will draw to You,
For I know that I am one with You.

22. Father, we love You

author unknown
arranged Margaret Evans

Worshipfully

1. Fa - ther, we love You, we wor - ship and a - dore You,

Glo - ri - fy Your name in all the earth.

Glo - ri - fy Your name, Glo - ri - fy Your name,

Glo - ri - fy Your name in all the earth.

2. Jesus, we love You . . . *etc.*
3. Spirit, we love You . . . *etc.*

23. Fellowship sweet

M. Wilkinson/R. Turner

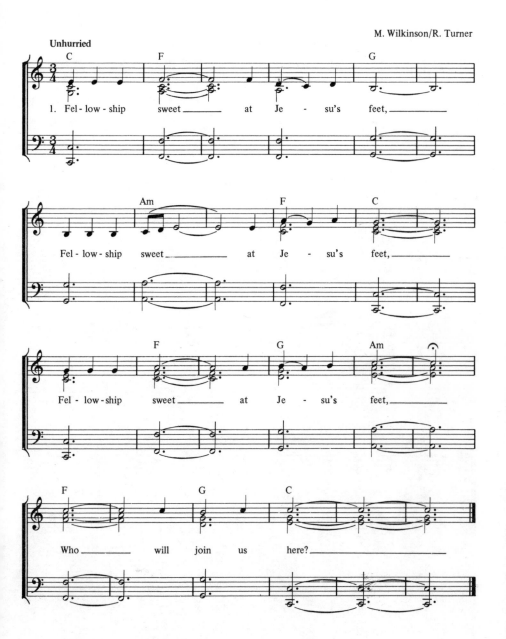

Unhurried

1. Fel-low-ship sweet _____ at Je - su's feet, _____
Fel-low-ship sweet _____ at Je - su's feet, _____
Fel-low-ship sweet _____ at Je - su's feet, _____
Who _____ will join us here? _____

2. Love we share when Jesus is there, *(three times)*
   . . . Who will join us here?

3. Money we share when Jesus is there, *etc.*

4. Bread and wine, with Jesus we'll dine, *etc.*

5. We love to sing to Jesus our King, *etc.*

24.   For as truly as I live

author unknown
arranged Margaret Evans

Capo 3 (C)

Steadily

For as tru-ly as I live all the earth shall be filled with the glo-ry of the Lord, For as tru-ly as I live all the earth shall be filled with the glo-ry of the Lord, The glo-ry, the glo-ry, the glo-ry of the Lord, For as tru-ly as I live all the earth shall be filled with the glo-ry of the Lord.

25. For I'm building a people of power

D. Richards

For I'm build-ing a peo-ple of pow-er___ And I'm mak-ing a peo-ple of praise, That will move thro' this land by My Spi-rit,___ And will glo-ri-fy My prec-ious Name. Build Your Church, Lord, Make us strong, Lord, Join our hearts, Lord, through Your Son. Make us one, Lord, in Your Bo-dy, In the King-dom of Your Son.___

26.

For we see Jesus

Capo 4 (C)

With majesty

Sue Hutchinson

For we see Je - sus____ en - throned on
high, Clothed in His right - eous-ness ____ we wor - ship
Him. Glo - ry and hon - our we give___ un - to
You, We see You in Your ho - li-ness and bow be-fore Your
throne. You are the Lord, ___ Your Name en-dures for
ev - er, ___ Je - sus the Name high ov - er all.

27.

Fountain, fountain
(His love has found a home in me)

P. Lawson-Johnston

drink - ing at the foun - tain, I've been swim- ming in the sea,

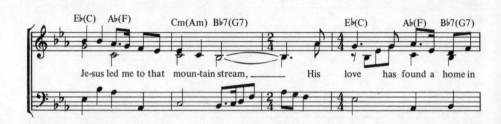

Je-sus led me to that moun-tain stream, _____ His love has found a home in

me, _____ O yes His love has found a home in me.

2. Water, water, flow through my heart,
    So many souls are dry,
    Lead me on from ankle deep
    To bathe in the ocean wide.
    Mountain, mountain, reach to the sky,
    Holy hands are raised,
    Before the Father's throne we bow
    In wonder, love and praise,
    In wonder, love and praise.

28. God will keep you

Capo 3 (G)

Betty Lou Mills

29. Great and marvellous

Bob Pitcher

Flowing

Great and _ mar-vel-lous are Thy works, O Lord God the Al-might-y,

Right-eous and true are Thy _ ways, O Thou King of the na - tion.

Who will not fear, O Lord, _____ And glo-ri-fy Thy name? ___ For

Thou a - lone art ho - ly and all the na-tions will come be - fore _ Thee and

wor - ship, wor - ship, wor - ship be - fore _ Thee, And

wor - ship, wor - ship, wor - ship be - fore _ Thee.

30. Hallelujah, for the Lord our God
(Hallelujah ... our God reigns)

Triumphantly

Dale Garratt

31. Hallelujah, praise the name of the Lord

32.   Happy are the people

M. Ray

Triumphantly

1. Hap-py are the people ____ who have learned to acclaim You Who walk, O Lord, in the light of Your presence. ____ In Your name ____ they shall re - joice all the day long Your righteousness shall lift them up. ____

Chorus

Hal - le - lu - jah! Hal - le - lu - jah! Hal - le - lu - jah! Hal - le - lu - jah! ____

2.   You are Yourself the strength in which we glory
     Through Your grace we hold our heads up high
     The Lord our God, He is our strength and shield
     The Holy One of Israel is our King.

33.

Hear my cry, O Lord
(In the shelter of His wings)

P. Lawson-Johnston

34.   Heavenly Father, I appreciate You

author unknown
arranged Margaret Evans

With quiet feeling

1. Hea-ven-ly Fa-ther, I app-re-ci-ate You.
Hea-ven-ly Fa-ther, I app-re-ci-ate You.
I love You, a-dore You, I bow down be-fore You, Hea-ven-ly Fa-ther, I app-re-ci-ate You.

2. Son of God, what a wonder You are,
   Son of God, what a wonder You are.
   You cleansed my soul from sin,
   You set the Holy Ghost within,
   Son of God, what a wonder You are.

3. Holy Ghost, what a comfort You are,
   Holy Ghost, what a comfort You are.
   You lead us, You guide us,
   You live right inside us,
   Holy Ghost, what a comfort You are.

35.

He holds the key

Joan Parsons

Steady pace

1. He holds the key to sal-va-tion, Je-sus is o-ver all. He is the Lord of cre-a-tion:

Chorus

Al - le - lu, Al - le - lu - ia. _____ Al - le - lu, Al - le - lu - ia Lord. _____

2. He is the Rock ever standing,
No man could break Him down.
He is the Truth everlasting:

3. He is a Light in the darkness,
All men shall see His face.
He breaks all chains to redeem us:

4. All power to Him who is mighty,
All praise to Him who is God.
All glory now and for ever:

36.

He is Lord

author unknown
arranged Margaret Evans

He is Lord, He is Lord, He is ri-sen from the dead and He is Lord. Ev-'ry

knee shall bow, ev-'ry tongue con - fess that Je - sus Christ is Lord.

37.

His name is higher

author unknown
arranged Margaret Evans

38. How can you love a spirit?
(Love me, love my brother)

B. Gillman

With pace

1. How can you love a spirit, How can you touch it with your hand? So how can you touch the Lord your God? Just give yourself to His command.

Chorus

Love me, love my bro-ther, That's the way God says it has to be. His Spi-rit is made flesh in His peo-ple, so you can love the Lord now in me.

2. It's easy to say we love Father,
   For he ain't hard to live with day by day.
   But it doesn't mean much to Him if we're neglecting
   To love one another come what may.

3. Have you ever felt you wanted to touch Jesus,
   But you never feel that you are getting through?
   Well here's a way that you can meet God surely,
   Just touch that brother sitting next to you.

39. How great is our God

author unknown
arranged Margaret Evans

Capo 3(D)

Joyfully

How great is our God, _____ How great is His name, _____ How great is His love _____ for ev-er the same. _____ He rolled back the wa - ters of the might-y Red Sea, _____ And He said, I'll nev-er leave you, _____ put your trust in Me. _____

40.   How lovely is Thy dwelling place

author unknown
arranged Margaret Evans

Capo 5 (C)

Joyfully

How love - ly is Thy dwell-ing place, O Lord of hosts, My soul longs and yearns _ for Your courts, _____ And my heart and flesh sing for joy to the liv - ing God. _____ One day in Thy pre - sence is far bet-ter to me than

41. How lovely on the mountains
(Our God reigns)

L. E. Smith Jnr.

Capo 1 (A)

Triumphantly with pace

1. How love - ly on the moun-tains are the feet of Him
Who brings good news, _____ good news,
Pro - claim - ing peace, an - nounc - ing news of hap-pi - ness, ____
[orig. version] An - nounc - ing peace, pro - claim - ing news of hap - pi - ness,
Our God reigns _____ Our God reigns. ____
[orig. version] Saying to Zi - on: Your God reigns.
Our God reigns _____ Our God reigns ____
[orig. version] Your God reigns Your God reigns

[orig. version]

Our God reigns _____ Our God reigns. _____

Your God reigns _____ Your God reigns.

Popular Version.

2.   You watchmen lift your voices joyfully as one,
      Shout for your King, your King.
      See eye to eye the Lord restoring Zion:
      Your God reigns, your God reigns!

3.   Waste places of Jerusalem break forth with joy,
      We are redeemed, redeemed.
      The Lord has saved and comforted His people:
      Your God reigns, your God reigns!

4.   Ends of the earth, see the salvation of your God,
      Jesus is Lord, is Lord.
      Before the nations He has bared His holy arm:
      Your God reigns, your God reigns!

Original Version.

2.   He had no stately form, He had no majesty,
      That we should be — drawn to Him.
      He was despised and we took no account of Him,
      Yet now He reigns — with the Most High.
             Chorus: Now He reigns   *(three times)*
                    With the Most High!

3.   It was our sin and guilt that bruised and wounded Him,
      It was our sin — that brought Him down.
      When we like sheep had gone astray, our Shepherd came
      And on His shoulders — bore our shame.
             Chorus: On His shoulders *(three times)*
                    He bore our shame.

4.   Meek as a lamb that's led out to the slaughterhouse,
      Dumb as a sheep — before its shearer,
      His life ran down upon the ground like pouring rain,
      That we might be — born again.
             Chorus: That we might be   *(three times)*
                    Born again.

5.   Out from the tomb He came with grace and majesty,
      He is alive — He is alive.
      God loves us so — see here His hands, His feet, His side,
      Yes, we know — He is alive.
             Chorus: He is alive!   *(four times)*

6.   How lovely on the mountains are the feet of Him
      Who brings good news, good news,
      Announcing peace, proclaiming news of happiness:
      Our God reigns, our God reigns.
             Chorus: Our God reigns!   *(four times)*

42.

If there be any love
(Be kind)

P. & D. Roe

Liltingly with steady pace

Chorus

If there be an-y love be-tween us, let's keep this in mind:____ Be kind,____ be kind,____ And if there's an-y un-der-stand-ing be-tween us let's keep this in mind,____ Be kind,____ Be kind,____ Be kind.

Verse

Am   **Em**   **F**   **C**

1. For a new com - mand-ment _____ I give un - to you, That you

Em   **C**   **F**   **G**

love one an - oth - er ev - en as I have loved you.

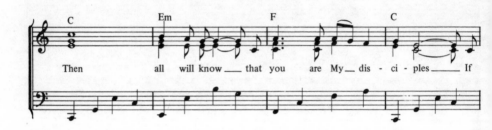

C   **Em**   **F**   **C**

Then all will know _____ that you are My _ dis - ci - ples _____ If

Em   **C**   **Dm7**   **G**   *D.S. al Fine*

you love _____ one an - oth - er. _____ So if there's

2. Love one another — that's what Jesus said,
So let's be kind and tenderhearted —
   to our brother who is our friend.
Let's live together — working out life in love,
Let's be sure our love endures — to the end.

3. Sometimes love can hurt us —
   and the pain of the truth is real,
But let's remember that our Father —
   is building His people with steel,
We are sons and daughters — children of the King,
So let's lay down our lives and feelings
   for our friends.

43. If your heart is right with my heart

Capo 5 (C)

G. Perrins

1. If your heart is right with my __ heart _____ give me your hand. _____
If your heart is right with my heart _____ give me your hand. _____
The right hand of fel-low - ship, The right hand of co-ve - nant; If your
heart is right with my __ heart _____ give me your hand. _____

2. If your heart is right with my heart,
Then we shall love;
If your heart is right with my heart,
Then we shall love.
We shall love in word and deed,
And be open to each need;
If your heart is right with my heart
Then we shall love.

3. If your heart is right with my heart,
We shall be one;
If your heart is right with my heart,
We shall be one.
One in heart and mind and soul,
One in purpose and in goal;
If your heart is right with my heart
We shall be one.

44. I get so excited, Lord
(I'm forgiven)

Capo 2 (G)

With pace and swing

M. Ray

1. I get so ex-cit-ed, Lord, ev-'ry time I re-a-lize _____ I'm for-gi - ven, _____ I'm for-gi-ven, _____ Je - sus Lord, You've done it all, You've paid the price. _____ I'm for-gi - ven, _____ I'm for-gi - ven. _____

Chorus

_____ Hal - le - lu - jah, Lord, my heart just fills with praise, _____

2. Living in Your presence, Lord, is life itself.
   I'm forgiven, I'm forgiven.
   With the past behind, grace for today
       and a hope to come.
   I'm forgiven, I'm forgiven.

45.   I give thanks, O Lord

P. Lawson-Johnston

For Thy stead-fast love and faith-ful - ness, Thy stead - fast love and

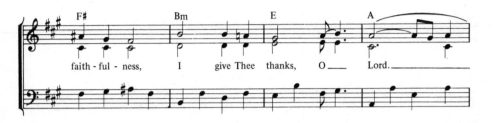

faith - ful - ness, I give Thee thanks, O ___ Lord. _____

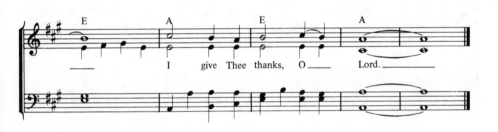

___ I give Thee thanks, O ___ Lord. _____

2. For Thou hast exalted above everything
   Thy name and Thy word on high,
   On the day I called, Thou didst answer me,
   My strength of soul Thou didst increase
   My strength of soul Thou didst increase.

3. Thou dost stretch out Thy hand against my foes,
   Thy right hand delivers me.
   The Lord will fulfil His purpose for me,
   Thy steadfast love endures for ever
   Thy steadfast love endures for ever.

46 I have built in My people
(I'm building a city)

Capo 3 (Am)

Joan Parsons

Flowing

I have built in my peo-ple a tem - ple, In you I live my good plea-sure to do, Yet I have more, lift your eyes and look fur - ther, For I am build - ing a ci-ty in you. ___ I'm build-ing a ci - ty, a peo-ple of po - wer, Filled with my glo - ry, re-flec-ting my light. You are that ci - ty and you shall be-hold me, show-ing all na -tions God reign-ing in might.

47.

I have loved you
(Arise, arise)

Capo 3 (C)

Y. Gale/M. Smith

1. I have loved you with an ev-er-last-ing love____ ____ And have cont-in-ued My faith-ful-ness___ to you.____ A-gain I will build___ you and you shall be built, And I will be your God, says the Lord.____ So a-

2. Again you'll adorn yourself with the timbrels,
    And go forth in the dance of the merrymakers,
    So plant your vineyards and you'll enjoy the fruit
    And I will be your God, says the Lord.

48.   I hear the sound of rustling

2. And all around the world the body waits expectantly,
   The promise of the Father is now ready to fall.
   The watchmen on the tower all exhort us to prepare
   And the church responds – a people who will answer the call.
   And this is not a phase which is passing,
   It's the start of an age that is to come.
   And where is the wise man and the scoffer?
   Before the face of Jesus they are dumb.

3. A body now prepared by God and ready for war,
   The prompting of the Spirit is our word of command.
   We rise, a mighty army, at the bidding of the Lord,
   The devils see and fear, for their time is at hand.
   And children of the Lord hear our commission
   That we should love and serve our God as one.
   The Spirit won't be hindered by division
   In the perfect work that Jesus has begun.

49.

I love You, Lord

Capo 3 (C)

Laurie Klein

With feeling

I love You, Lord, ___ and I lift my voice ___ To

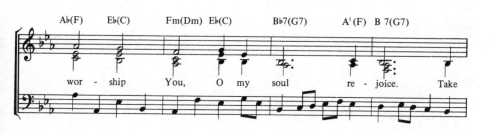

wor - ship You, O my soul re - joice. Take

joy, my King, ___ in ___ what You hear, ___ May it be a

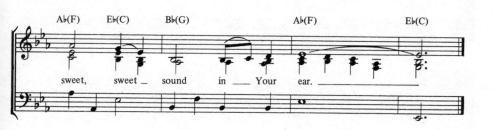

sweet, sweet _ sound in ___ Your ear. ___

50. I'm redeemed

T. Humphries

With pace and swing

I'm re - deemed, Yes I am, by the blood of the Lamb, Je-sus Christ has done it all for me. I am His, He is mine, I'm part of the roy-al vine, All my sins were washed a - way at Cal-va-ry.

Fine

Once I was lost, I had no - where to go, my life was just a lone - ly round of sin. Till Je-sus said to me, By My blood shed on the tree I've paid the price, bought you back, you're Mine, oh what a friend!

D.C. al Fine

51.   I'm saved by the grace of God

I. Traynar

With feeling
Verse

1. I'm saved _____ by the grace of God, _____

Root-ed _____ and fixed in love, _____ and I'm fi - nished _____

_____ with my old life. _____ I'm a - live _____ in a brand new

Chorus

way _____ And it's ea - sy to live now, _____ I've gi - ven my

all, _____ Sur - rend- ered ____ ev - 'ry - thing to You.____

_____ I have no rights on my life,____

_____ O Je - sus, _____ You are my Lord.____

2. I know I have died to sin,
Baptised into His glorious death;
I've been raised up into newness of life,
I'm no longer a slave to sin.

3. I live now by the law of God
Written on my heart,
And the Spirit and my brothers
Are showing me where I've got to change.

4. My life is hid with Christ in God,
I know I am secure
And nothing can separate me
From the love which is in Christ.

52.

In these last days

T. Humphries

Peacefully

In these last days I'll be with my child-ren.
And in my church my glo-ry will shine,
They all shall be my ve-ry own re-flec-tion,
And all the earth shall know that they are mine.

53.   I receive Your love

Paul Armstrong

Gently

1. I re-ceive Your love, I re-ceive Your love, In my heart I re-ceive Your love, O Lord. I re-ceive Your love by Your Spi-rit with-in me, I re-ceive, I re-ceive Your love.

2. I confess Your love,
I confess Your love,
From my heart I confess Your love, O Lord.
I confess Your love
By Your Spirit within me,
I confess, I confess Your love.

54.

I see the Lord

author unknown
arranged Margaret Evans

With warmth

I see the Lord, __ I see the Lord, __ He is high and lift-ed up and His train fills the tem-ple, ___ He is high and lift-ed up ___ and His train fills the tem-ple. ___ The an-gels cry, Ho-ly, ___ the an-gels cry, Ho-ly, ___ the an-gels cry, Ho-ly is the Lord. ___

55. I stand before the presence

Capo 5 (C)

Thoughtfully

Mavis Ford

I stand be-fore the pres-ence of the Lord God of hosts, A child of my Fath-er and an heir of His grace, _____ For Je - sus paid the debt for me, the veil was torn in two, And the Ho - ly of Ho - lies has be - come my dwel - ling place.

56. It is no longer I that liveth

Sally Ellis

57.   It's so good, my Lord

Capo 3 (G)

Happily
Chorus

M. Ray

It's so good, my Lord, Liv-ing my life in You. For Your yoke is ea-sy and Your bur-den is light Feels so

1. Joy of for-give-ness,

2. Knowing I'm loved, Lord, standing in Your grace,
   Reigning in life, running the race.

58. It's so good to thank You, Lord

B. Trickett

It's so good to thank You, Lord, It's so good to thank You, It's good to give You (our) thanks for ev-'ry-thing. —

thanks un-to the King. So I'll thank You in the morn-ing and I'll thank You a-gain at night, I'll thank You for Your kind-ness and I'll thank You for Your faith-ful-ness.

59. I want to learn to appreciate You

Capo 3 (C)

J. Kennett

With pace and swing

Often sung colloquially *I wanna learn to . . .* etc.

60. I want to sing about my Jesus
(As eternity begins)

P. Lawson-Johnston/P. Somerville

1. I want to sing a-bout my Je - sus, I want to sing a-bout my Lord, I want to tell you of His King-dom and His bles - sings a - broad. We are new, we are ho - ly, We are washed, we are

Chorus

Glo-ry, Glo-ry, Glo-ry, Glo-ry, How I love the King of glo-ry, We sing of Je-sus and His

Glo-ry, Glory, Hal-le-lu-jah, Ho-ly, Holy, Ho-ly, Holy, Ho-ly is the King of glo-ry. We sing of

Je-sus and His love, _____ love, _____ love, _____

love. _____ ___ Sing of His love. _____

2. I want to meet Him on the mountain;
I want to stand before His throne.
He has asked me to His table
To share the beauty of His home.

We are welcome, we are chosen,
Children in His family.
I never cease to gaze in wonder
At what He has revealed to me.

So, can I share with you my Jesus;
Share with you my precious Lord.
Let me lead you to the Kingdom.
He is the way, He is the door.

61. I was once in darkness

Two-part round

Joan Parsons

Lyrics:

I was once in dark-ness, Now my eyes can see, I was lost but Je-sus sought and found me. O what love He off-ers, O what peace He gives, I will sing for ev-er-more, He lives.

Hal-le-lu-jah Je-sus! Hal-le-lu-jah Lord! Hal-le-lu-jah Fa-ther, I am shield-ed by His word. I will live for ev-er, I will nev-er die, I will rise up to meet Him in the sky.

62.
I will enter His gates

author unknown
arranged Margaret Evans

63. I will extol You

Sue Hutchinson/Wendy Churchill

Capo 5 (C)

Brightly

Lyrics:

I will ex-tol You, my God and my King, I will bless Your Name for ev-er and ev-er. Ev-'ry day will I bless You, O Lord, I will glo-ri-fy Your Name for ev-er-more. For You are great and high-ly to be praised, We shall de-clare Your mighty acts, We shall tell of Your good-ness and kind-ness to us, Our mouths shall speak the praise of our God.

64. I will magnify Your name, O Lord

D. Bolton

2. I will magnify Your name, O Lord, Hallelujah!
I will drink of the well of Your love, Hallelujah!
With instrument and with voice, Hallelujah!
My spirit in You shall rejoice, Hallelujah!

3. I will magnify Your name, O Lord, Hallelujah!
I will drink of the well of Your love, Hallelujah!
With the timbrel and the dance, Hallelujah!
My love for You I shall express, Hallelujah!

4. I will magnify Your name, O Lord, Hallelujah!
I will drink of the well of Your love, Hallelujah!
I will worship You to the end of my days, Hallelujah!
With a heart that is full of praise, Hallelujah!

65.   I will run after You

Thoughtfully

Anne Denton

I will run af - ter You with all my heart,

I will run af - ter You with all my strength,

Like the deer search-ing for cold wa - ter in a drought

I thirst for You with all my heart,

Like the deer search-ing for cold wa - ter in a drought

I thirst for You with all my heart.

66. I will sing unto the Lord

author unknown
arranged Margaret Evans

Easy waltz feel

I will sing un-to the Lord as long as I live,

I will sing praise to my God while I have my be-ing, _____

_____ My me - di - ta - tion of Him

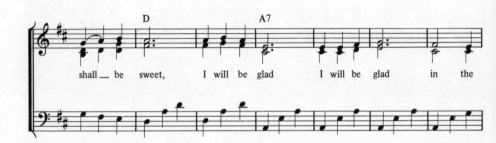

shall __ be sweet, I will be glad I will be glad in the

67.   Jesus, come closer now to me

Pat Bilbrough

Je - sus, come clo - ser now to me, _____ I am reach-ing out, ___ for You I need to see; _____ no more just words and facts ___ a - bout a man who lived long a - go, _____ Je - sus it's You I rea - lly need to know. _____

68.   Jesus, how lovely You are

2.   Hallelujah, Jesus died and rose again;
Hallelujah, Jesus forgave all my sin.

3.   Hallelujah, Jesus is meek and lowly;
Hallelujah, Jesus is pure and holy.

4.   Hallelujah, Jesus is the Bridegroom;
Hallelujah, Jesus will take His Bride soon.

69.

Jesus I come

T. Humphries

Je-sus I come and I fall at Your feet ___ to kiss those deep wounds borne for me. ___ I feel my heart sing at Your pres-ence so sweet, ___ my lips trem-ble in mel-o-dy. ___ Come and fill me a-new, let me dwell in You too, Make me one in the Spi-rit with Thee. ___ As I call on Your name I am so glad You came and died, rose a-gain and saved me. ___

70.

Jesus is changing me

A. Huntley

2. Then shall the blessing of the Lord come down,
When we give all to Him;
And we shall go forth in holiness
Delighting ourselves in God.

71.   Jesus is Lord!

Capo 1 (G)

With majesty

David Mansell

1. Jesus is Lord! Creation's voice proclaims it,
For by His power each tree and flower was planned and made.
Jesus is Lord! the universe declares it,
Sun, moon and stars in heaven cry

Chorus
'Jesus is Lord!' Jesus is Lord! Jesus is Lord!
Praise Him with Hallelujahs for Jesus is Lord!

2. Jesus is Lord! yet from His throne eternal
In flesh He came to die in pain
On Calv'ry's tree.
Jesus is Lord! from Him all life proceeding,
Yet gave His life a ransom
Thus setting us free.

3. Jesus is Lord! o'er sin the mighty conqueror,
From death He rose, and all His foes
Shall own His Name.
Jesus is Lord! God sent His Holy Spirit
To show by works of power
That Jesus is Lord.

72.

Jesus, Jesus, Jesus

author unknown
arranged Margaret Evans

Capo 3 (G)

Je - sus, Je - sus, Je - sus, Your
love has mel - ted my heart.
Je - sus, Je - sus, Je - sus, Your
love has mel - ted my heart.

73.   Jesus, Name above all names

Naida Hearn
and Patricia Cain

Worshipfully

Je - sus, Name a - bove all names, Beau - ti - ful Sav - iour, Glo - ri - ous Lord; Em - man - u - el, God _ is with us, Bless- ed Re - deem - er. Liv - ing Word.

74.

Jesus, stand among us

Capo 3 (C)

G. Kendrick

2. So to You we're gathering out of each and every land,
    Christ the love between us at the joining of our hands;
    O, Jesus, we love You, so we gather here,
    Join our hearts in unity and take away our fear.

75.

Jesus take me as I am

Capo 4 (C)

D. Bryant

Je - sus take me as I am, I can come no oth-er way. Take me deep-er in to You, Make my flesh life melt a - way.

76.　　Jesus, thank You, Jesus

77. Jubilate, everybody
(Jubilate Deo)

Fred Dunn

78. Let God arise

I. Smith

Let God a - rise u - pon this ho - ly moun - tain, Come sing to Him O king - doms of the earth. He gives power and strength un - to His peo - ple, Sing praise to Him, Sing prai - ses to His name.

79. Let Me have My way among you
(Do not strive)

G. Kendrick

Thoughtfully

1. Let Me have My way a - mong____ you, Do not strive, do not strive. strive. For Mine is the pow - er and the glo - ry For ev - er and ev - er the same.

Let Me have My way a - mong____ you, Do not strive, Do not strive.

2. We'll let You have Your way among us,
We'll not strive, we'll not strive. *Repeat.*
For Yours is the power and the glory
For ever and ever the same.
We'll let You have Your way among us,
We'll not strive, we'll not strive.

3. Let My peace rule within your hearts,
Do not strive, do not strive. *Repeat.*
For Mine is the power and the glory
For ever and ever the same.
Let My peace rule within your hearts,
Do not strive, do not strive.

4. We'll let Your peace rule within our hearts,
We'll not strive, we'll not strive. *Repeat.*
For yours. . . *etc.*

80.

Let there be love

D. Bilbrough

Triumphantly

Let there be love shared a - mong us, let there be love in our

eyes, May now Your love sweep this na - tion, Cause us O

Lord ____ to a - rise. Give us a fresh un - der -

stand - ing of bro - ther - ly love that is real, Let there be

love shared a - mong us, Let there be love. ____

81. Let us open up ourselves

P.Bilbrough

Flowing

Chorus

Let us o - pen up our - selves to one an - oth -

er with-out fear of be-ing hurt or turned a - way;_____ For we

need to con-fess our weak-ness-es,__ To be co-vered by our bro-ther's love, To be

real and learn our true i - den - ti - ty._____

Verse

1. For we are all a part of one an - oth - er,_____ We

can-not hope to live life ful - ly on our own;_____ We

each pos-sess a prec-ious part — of our Fa-ther's na - ture, And to

-ge - ther we'll be - come that per - fect whole.— So let us

2. And God shall surely build His living temple
   Of people set completely free,
   Loving and appreciating one another,
   Enjoying life in its entirety.

3. Many shall be drawn to us and wonder
   At the peace and the love and the joy that will never die;
   They will drink from that stream of living water
   Flowing out from the fulness of our lives.

4. So help us to understand each other in a new and living way,
   Not just accepting words that are spoken in themselves,
   But by speaking more freely and listening more clearly
   We shall understand the spirit that's within.

82. Lift Jesus higher

author unknown
arranged Margaret Evans

Lift Je-sus high-er, Lift Je-sus high-er, Lift Him up for the world to see.— He said if

I be lift - ed up from the earth I will draw all men un-to Me.—

Arr. Copyright © 1980 Thankyou Music, P.O. Box 75, Eastbourne BN23 6NW

83. Lord God, heavenly King

Capo 4 (C)

Worshipfully

Sue Hutchinson

Lord God,_____ hea-ven-ly King,_____

You are our God,_____ To You we sing;_____

Re-ceive the wor-ship of our hearts,_____ the a-dor-a-tion of our

lips; How we love____ You, Lord God, hea-ven-ly King._____

84.
Lord, I feel

Smoothly
Chorus

D. Bolton

Lord, _____ I feel _____ Your sweet

pre - sence wher - ev- er I go. _____ Lord, _____

_____ I _____ feel _____ Your sweet pre-sence wher - ev - er I

go. _____ go. _____

2.	If I should fail and feel despair,
	You lift me up above all my care.

3.	Lord, I love You and I know that You love me,
	I feel Your love embracing me.

85.

Lord, I want to know
(More of You)

M. Ray

86.

Lord Jesus, we enthrone You

Capo 2 (G)

With reverence

Paul Kyle

Lord Je - sus,__ we en - throne__ You,__

we pro - claim You our King,__

Stand - ing here__ in the midst of us__

__ we raise You up__ with our

87. Lord, please make Your people one

A. Woodroffe/C. Head

2. All around the kingdoms fall,
   But we hear our Father call —
   You are safe, My children, with Me.
   Show My love, for I want the world to see.

3. Lord, You're making Your people one,
   And answering the prayer of Your dear Son,
   That the world may see that we are one,
   And give the glory unto You.

88.   Lord, we want to thank You

Capo 3 (D)

Unhurried   Dougie Brown

Lord, we want to thank You for Your love for us, ____ That sweet love that watch-es ov - er us each day. ____ Lord, re-lease our spi - rits so our praise can flow to You, Now we lift our hands to wor - ship You. ____

89. Love one another

N. Rose

Love one an-oth-er as I have loved you,___ Be right-eous, be ho - ly, in all that you do. Just seek Me, lis-ten to___Me, with all your heart fol-low Me, and I pro-mise you shall ___ not ___ fall. ___ And I pro-mise you shall ___ not ___ fall. ___ So

90. Make a joyful noise

C. Head

Cheerfully

1. Make a joy-ful noise un-to the Lord, all ye lands, all ye lands.

Make a joy-ful noise un-to the Lord, all ye lands, all ye lands.

Come be-fore Him with sing-ing,— Come be-fore Him with joy.————

Make a joy-ful noise un-to the Lord, all ye lands, all ye lands.

2. Open your hearts before Him now.
Give Him your praise, give Him your praise.
Open your hearts before Him now.
Give Him your praise, give Him your praise.
Come before Him with singing, *etc.*

91.

My heart overflows

With warmth
Chorus

Caroline Govier

My heart ov - er - flows with a good - - ly ___ theme, I will add- ress my ver - ses to the King; ___ My heart ov - er - flows with ___ praise to my God, I'll give Him the love of my heart.

last time
Fine

Verse

2.   For He has chosen Mount Zion as His resting place,
           He says, 'Here will I dwell,
           I will abundantly bless and satisfy,
           And her saints will shout for joy.

3.   'Lift up your eyes round about and see,
           Your heart shall thrill and rejoice,
           For the abundance of the nations is coming to you,
           I am glorifying My house.'

92. My life is really blessed

A. Huntley

Joyfully
Chorus

My life is real-ly blessed be-cause I know the love of God

And I can be so free to live and move within that

love; Part of His fa - mi - ly,

Liv - ing in vic - to - ry, Se - cure in know - ing that

Je - sus has got ev - 'ry - thing in hand.

Verse

1. Some-times I won-der if I'll e - ver get through,

And I see my life's in need of chang-ing, _____

But though He dis - ci -plines, it's al - ways in love, ___

And so with con - fid- ence I say _____

D.C. al Fine

2. So I'm really happy to be walking with God
   Knowing His care from day to day,
   He is the answer to my every desire,
   And so with confidence I say. . .

93. My Lord He is the fairest of the fair

Joan Parsons

94. My Lord, You are so good to me

Capo 3 (G)

Flowing

Intro.

P. & D. Roe

My Lord, _____ You are so good to me _____ and I'll love You as long as I live _____ And I'll try _____ each _ day that I live _____ to bless You and bring joy _ to Your heart. _____ My

95.

My peace

K. Routledge

Gently ♪= 120

1. My peace ___ I give ___ un-to you, ___ It's a
peace ___ that the world ___ can-not give, ___ It's a peace ___ that the
world ___ can-not un - der - stand. Peace to know,
peace to live. ___ My peace ___ I give ___ un-to you.

2. My joy I give unto you,
   It's a joy that the world cannot give,
   It's a joy that the world cannot understand.
   Joy to know, joy to live.
   My joy I give unto you.

3. My love I give unto you,
   It's a love that the world cannot give,
   It's a love that the world cannot understand.
   Love to know, love to live.
   My love I give unto you.

96.

O Father, I do love You

Dave Bolton

2. O Jesus, I adore You, *(three times)*
    Hallelujah, Hallelujah.

3. O Spirit, I do bless You, *(three times)*
    Hallelujah, Hallelujah.

97.   O give thanks

Joanne Pond

With pace

O give thanks to the Lord, all you His
peo-ple, O give thanks to the Lord for He is good.
Let us praise, let us thank, let us ce - le - brate and
dance, O give thanks to the Lord for He is good.

98.   O Lord most Holy God

Worshipfully

Wendy Churchill

1. O Lord most Holy God, Great are Your purposes,
Great is Your will for us, Great is Your love.
And we rejoice in You, And we will sing to You,
O Father have Your way, Your will be done.

2. For You are building
A temple without hands,
A city without walls
Enclosed by fire.
A place for You to dwell,
Built out of living stones,
Shaped by a Father's hand
And joined in love.

99.

O Lord, my Lord

Capo 2 (C)

Diane Fung

O Lord, my Lord, how ma-jes-tic You are;
When I be-hold Your face, I know I have life.
No words can de-clare how much You mean to me,
You make my heart sing As you fill me a - gain. How maj-es-tic You are.

100. O Lord, You've done great things

Joyfully with pace

Caroline Govier

O Lord, You've done great things, And I will praise You, I will ex - tol You and mag-ni-fy Your Name. O Lord, You've done great things, And I will praise You, I will ex - tol You and mag - ni - fy Your Name.

101. Our eyes have seen the King

Caroline Govier

With majesty

1. Our eyes have seen the King ___ seat-ed on Da-vid's throne, ___ and of ___ His ___ king - dom there shall be no end, ___ for the zeal of the Lord of ___ hosts ___ has es - tab-lished it for e - ver - more. ___

2. The Lord is great in Zi - on, the ci - ty of our God, ___ He has found-ed it to be His ___ dwell-ing that His will may be known on earth ___ and His ways known a - mong all ___ na - tions, for none is great like our God. ___

102.

Perfect love

P. Lawson-Johnston

Unhurried

1. Per-fect love, Per-fect love means that Je-sus is near.
Per-fect love, Per-fect love means no room for my fear.
With-out warn-ing a song seems to — rise in my heart, as love
finds a home, seek-ing to — set me a-part for Jesus a - lone, _____ for Je - sus a - lone. _____

2. Perfect love, perfect love means that Jesus is here.
Perfect love, perfect love is the cross I must bear.
As a seed is sown I must fall to the ground
And I must learn to die,
Surrender myself to the sound
Of Jesus first not I,
Of Jesus first not I.

103.   Praise the Lord together

author unknown
arranged Margaret Evans

Praise the Lord to-ge-ther sing-ing A - lle-lu-ia A - lle-lu - ia A - lle - lu-ia.

104. Praise You, Lord

N. Rose

Capo 3 (C)

With majesty

1. Praise You, Lord, for the won-der of Your heal-ing. Praise You, Lord, for Your love so free-ly given, out-pour-ing a-noin-ting, flow-ing in to heal our wounds. Praise You, Lord, for Your love for me.

2. Praise You, Lord, for Your gift of liberation.
   Praise You, Lord, You have set the captives free;
   The chains that bind are broken by the sharpness of Your sword,
   Praise You, Lord, You gave Your life for me.

3. Praise You, Lord, You have born the depths of sorrow.
   Praise You, Lord, for Your anguish on the tree;
   The nails that tore Your body and the pain that tore Your soul.
   Praise You, Lord, Your tears, they fell for me.

4. Praise You, Lord, You have turned our thorns to roses.
   Glory, Lord, as they bloom upon Your brow.
   The path of pain is hallowed, for Your love has made it sweet,
   Praise You, Lord, and may I love You now.

105. Praise Your name, Lord Jesus

T. Humphries

Praise Your name, Lord Je-sus, Praise Your name, King of kings and Lord of lords. _____ Praise Your name, Lord Je-sus, Praise Your name, King of kings and Lord of lords. _____ _

High-er than _ the high-est, The rich-est and _ the best,

Praise Your name, Lord Je-sus, It's Your name I've con-fessed to be my Sa-viour.

106.   Rejoice in the Lord always

Two-part round

Capo 3(C)

author unknown
arranged Margaret Evans

107.   River wash over me

Capo 3 (C)

Unhurried (with strength)

Dougie Brown

1. Riv - er___ wash ov - er me, ___
Cleanse me and make me new.
Bathe me, re - fresh me and fill me a - new,
Ri - ver___ wash o - ver me.

2. Spirit watch over me,
   Lead me to Jesus' feet.
   Cause me to worship and fill me anew,
   Spirit watch over me.

3. Jesus rule over me,
   Reign over all my heart.
   Teach me to praise you and fill me anew,
   Jesus rule over me.

108.

Seek ye the Lord
(Peace like a river)

Joan Parsons

1. Seek ye the Lord _ all ye peo-ple, _ Turn to Him while He is near. _ Let the wick-ed for-sake his own way and call on Him while He may hear. _ Ho ev-'ry-one _ who is thir-sty, _ Come to the wa-ters of life, _ Come and drink of the milk _ and the wine, _ Come with-out mo-ney and_ price.

2. For you shall go out in joy
and be led forth in peace.
The mountains and hills before you shall sing
and the trees of the field clap their hands.
Instead of the thorns shall come cyprus,
and myrtle replace every brier.
And it shall be to remember the Lord
an everlasting sign.

109. Set my spirit free

author unknown
arranged Margaret Evans

Worshipfully

Set my spi-rit free that I might wor - ship Thee,

Set my spi-rit free that I might praise Thy Name.

Let all bond-age go and let de - li - v'rance flow,

Set my spi - rit free to wor-ship Thee._____

110. Sing praises to the Lord

111. Sing unto God

Dave Richards

Sing unto God for He is ex - alt - ed,
Sing un - to Him, Sing un - to Him.
Lift high His name for He is vic - tor - ious,
Sing un - to Him, Sing un - to Him.

112. Sing unto the Lord a new song

M. Ray

Sing un - to the Lord a new song,

Sing un - to the Lord, all the earth. Sing to the

Lord, bless His name. He is great-ly to be praised.

Sing un - to the Lord a new song.

113. Some folks may ask me
(He is my everything)

Sally Ellis

Some folks may ask me, ___ Some folks may say, ___ Who is this
Je - sus ___ you talk a - bout ev - 'ry day? He is my Sav - iour, ___ He set me
free, ___ now lis - ten while I tell you ___ what He means to me. ___
___ He is my ev - 'ry - thing, ___ He is my all, ___ He is my ev - 'ry - thing ___
___ both great and small. ___ He made my life com - plete, ___ made ev - 'ry - thing
new. ___ He is my ev - 'ry - thing, ___ now how a - bout you? ___

114.   Sweet fellowship

R. Wilson

With pace

1. Sweet_____ fel-low-ship, Je-sus in_the midst. Life blos-soms in the Church,_ men by men are blessed When Je-sus_ is in_____ the midst._____ _____ I've ne-ver known a time like this, Feel the spi-rit with-in_ me rise, Come and see what God is do-ing, Lord, we love You.__

2. Peace and harmony — Jesus reigning here;
   The Church moves at His command,
   No room for doubt or fear
   For Jesus is reigning here.

   I've never known a time like this,
   Feel the spirit within me rise.
   Come and see what God is doing,
   Lord, we love You. . . .

3. Sweet fellowship, Jesus in the midst,
   Life blossoms in the Church.
   Men by men are blessed
   When Jesus is in the midst.

115. Take My yoke upon you

116. Thank You, Jesus, for Your love to me

A. Huntley

Thank You, Je - sus, _____ for Your love to me. _____

_____ Thank You, Je - sus, _____ for Your grace so free. _____

_____ I'll lift my voice to praise Your name, Praise You a-gain and a-

gain. You are ev - 'ry - thing, _____ You are my Lord. _____

117. Thank You Jesus, praise You Jesus

Tom Hamilton

Thank You Je - sus, ___ praise You Je - sus ___ for Your
con - stant love to me. ___ I want to
thank ___ You, ___ I want to praise ___ You ___ just for
be - ing a friend to me. ___
last time ___ just for be - ing a friend to me. ___

118. The Church of God

The Church of God is not stee-ples,_____ house meet-ings or ca-the-drals. But the Church of God is peo-ple_____ whose hearts have be-come the dwell-ing place of God in the Spi-rit;___ Walk-ing in the light with God and one an-oth-er, be-ing built to-ge-ther_____

119.

The joy of my salvation

Robin Hawkins

Capo 3 (C)

Chorus The joy of my sal - va - tion is the joy of know-ing You, Your sweet pres-ence near to me is the strength that holds me true.

Verse 1. When You're near I see Your hand in so man-y lit-tle things, And each mo-ment that I share with You helps my faith grow big-ger wings. The

2. That feeling when You're near, Lord,
I want nothing to destroy,
And I'll not flirt with any sin
That would take away my joy.

3. When You're near I'm confident
That I'm following Your Son,
And the things I ask I know You'll grant
Because our hearts are one.

4. When You're near I see so clear
What things are right and wrong,
And that makes me glad for I'd not do
Anything to grieve Your Son.

120. The kingdom of this world

Capo 4 (C)

P. Fung

Slow and easy

The king - dom of this world has be-come _ the

King - dom of our God and of His Christ _ And

He shall reign for e - ver and e - ver.

121. The law of the Lord

author unknown
arranged Margaret Evans

Capo 3 (C)
Brightly

1. The law of the Lord is per-fect, ___ converting the soul, ___ The testimony of the Lord is sure, ___ mak-ing wise the sim-ple. ___ More to be de-sired are they than gold, yea than much fine gold, ___ sweet-er al-so than ho-ney ___ and the ho — ney comb. ___ More to be de-sired are they than gold, yea than much fine gold, ___ sweet-er al-so than ho-ney ___ and the ho-ney - comb. ___

2. The statutes of the Lord are right, rejoicing the heart,
   The commandment of the Lord is pure, enlightening the eyes.

3. The fear of the Lord is clean, enduring for ever,
   The judgements of the Lord are true and righteous altogether.

122.

The Lord bless thee

A song to share

men = tails down
women = tails up

Chuck Butler

123. The Lord has built up Zion

Capo 4 (C)

Wendy Churchill

124.

The Lord reigns

2. The floods have lifted up, O Lord,
   Lifted up their voice,
   Mightier than the thunder of the waves,
   The Lord on high is mighty.

125. The nations shall see you justified

With steady strength

Paul Wakely

The na - tions shall see you jus - ti - fied, and all the kings your
glo - ry, and you shall be called by a new name which the mouth of the Lord shall
give. You shall be a crown of beau - ty in the hand of the
Lord and a roy - al di - a - dem in the hand of God.
And you shall be called ho - ly ones, the re - deemed of the Lord, and
you shall be called sought out, a ci - ty not for - sa - ken.

126. The promised land

Capo 3 (C)

With pace

P. Iszatt

1. The prom-ised land God gave us is right here at our feet
So let us build the ci-ty till hea-ven is complete. The ground on which we're stand-ing
on-ly we can mould, U-nique in ev-'ry touch
we make, yet blend-ing with the whole. Your

Chorus

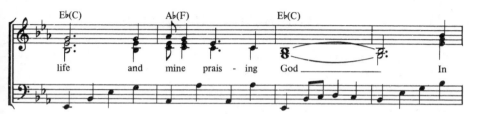

life and mine prais - ing God _____ In

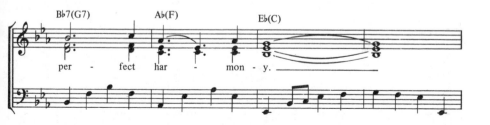

per - fect har - mon - y.

O come dear Fa - ther ___ please live with us, ___ Re -

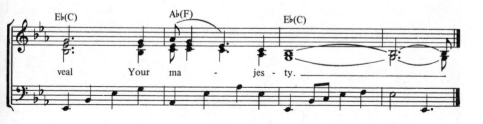

veal Your ma - jes - ty. _____

2. Behold the holy city,
   The new Jerusalem,
   Coming down from heaven,
   God's dwelling place with men.
   The bride and groom together,
   Eternity is sealed,
   And in the new creation
   God's heart and ours fulfilled.

3. See there is no temple
   To go and worship in:
   The Lamb and the Almighty
   Fill every living thing;
   And in the glory of their light,
   Flowing from the throne,
   A stream of living water,
   God's holiness, our home.

127.
Therefore the redeemed

Capo 3 (G)

With pace and swing

Ruth Lake

There-fore the re - deemed of the Lord shall re - turn and come with sing - ing ___ un - to Zi - on, ___ and ev - er - last - ing ___ joy shall be up - on their head. There-fore the re - head. They shall ob - tain

128. There is no condemnation

Joan Parsons

With feeling

1. There is no con-demna-tion for those who are in Christ ____

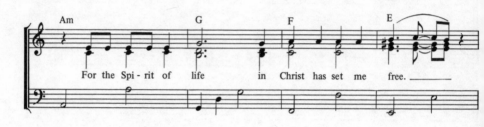

For the Spi-rit of life in Christ has set me free. ____

Chorus

O He's a-live, He's a-live, He's a-live. ____ O He's a-

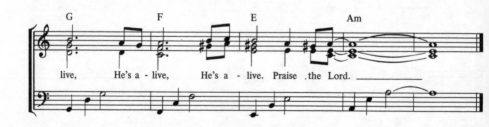

live, He's a-live, He's a-live. Praise the Lord. ____

2. If the Spirit of Him who raised Christ from the dead
   Be born in you, then He will give you life.

3. If God be for us, who can be against us?
   For He who sent His Son will freely give us all things.

129.

This is His body
(Communion song)

Claire White

130.

This is the day

author unknown
arranged Margaret Evans

Brightly with pace

This is the day, This is the day that the Lord has made, that the
Lord has made; We shall re-joice, We shall re-joice and be
glad in it, and be glad in it. This is the day that the
Lord has __ made, we shall re-joice and be glad in __ it;
This is the day, this is the day that the Lord has made.

131. Tho' the fig tree shall not blossom
(Hinds' feet)

P. Lawson-Johnston

2. Though the fields shall yield no food,
   And the flock shall lose the fold,
   And there shall be no herd found in the stall.

132. Thou art worthy to take the book

Capo 1 (G)

With majesty

T. Pullen

Thou art wor-thy to take the book and to op-en its seals, for
Thou wast slain and by Thy blood didst ran-som men for
God, From ev-'ry tribe and tongue and peo-ple and
na-tion and hast made them a king-dom and priests to our God, and
they shall reign, shall reign on earth.

133.　Thy loving kindness

author unknown
arranged Margaret Evans

Capo 3 (C)

Happily

1. Thy lov-ing kind - ness ____ is bet-ter than life, ____ Thy lov-ing

kind - ness __ is bet-ter than life. ____ My lips shall praise Thee, __ thus will I

bless Thee, __ Thy lov-ing kind- ness is bet- ter than life.

2.　I lift my hands up unto Thy name,
　　I lift my hands up unto Thy name.
　　My lips shall praise Thee, thus will I bless Thee,
　　Thy loving kindness is better than life.

134.   Thy throne, O God

Capo 3 (C)

David Mansell

135.   Unto Thee do I lift my eyes

P. Simmons

136. Victory

Capo 3 (G)

Diane Fung

Vic - to - ry is on our lips and in our lives, For Je - sus has sure - ly been raised from the dead, and ne - ver shall the powers of dark - ness doubt that Je - sus is

137.
Wait on the Lord

Capo 3 (C)

Peacefully

Chuck Butler

Wait on the Lord and be of good cou-rage, and

He shall streng - then thine heart.

Wait, _____ I say wait on the Lord, and

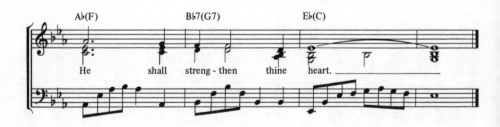

He shall streng - then thine heart. _____

138.   We acknowledge You

Sue Griffin

We ack - now - ledge You — Je - sus as our King,
To — You we can sur - ren - der ev - 'ry - thing,
For we know that in Your love You will bless us from a -
bove, and we wor - ship You Lord Je - sus as our King.

139.   We are being built into a temple

We are be-ing built in-to a tem-ple,
Fit for God's own dwell-ing place;
In-to the house of God which is the Church,
the pill-ar

140. We are chosen, we are redeemed

Capo 3 (C)

Joan Parsons

Steadily

1. We are cho - sen, ___ we are re - deemed. ___

We are cho - sen, ___ we are re - deemed. ___

Sons and daugh - ters ___ of our Lord, ___

We are cho - sen, ___ we are re - deemed. ___

2. We are going to be like Him,
   We are going to be like Him,
   Pure and holy, crystal clear,
   We are going to be like Him.

3. We are living to praise our King,
   We are living to praise our King,
   Feel His glory, fill the earth,
   We are living to praise our King.

141. We are gathering together

Capo 3 (C)

I. Traynar

With pace and swing

We are ga-ther - ing to-ge - ther Un-to the King of kings,
Come in the Spi - rit with joy__ and peace, __ Fill your heart with a song of glad-ness for all He's done, __ Come bless the Lord, come on and bless the Lord. Let your spi - rit flow__

142. We are God's own army

Capo 3 (C)

Joan Parsons

Steady pace

1. We are God's own ar - my, chil - dren of His Son,
Bro - thers in His King - dom, by His Spi - rit born. For our
God is King, yes our God is King, For our
God is King, glo - ry to His name.

2. Moving as His body we shall claim that land
   He has set before us by His mighty hand.

3. Then shall God's own glory fill the earth abroad,
   Nations shall proclaim Him Christ and Lord of all.

143.

We are moving on

Capo 1 (D)

I. Traynar

1. We are mov-ing on in-to a deep ap-pre-ci-a-tion___ of the love which flows from Fa-ther out to ev-'ry child of God,___ Of the grace with which He hand-les ev-'ry mi-nute sit-u-a-tion, How He

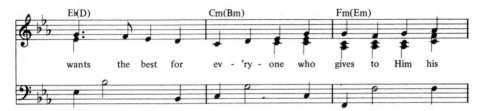

wants the best for ev - 'ry - one who gives to Him his

Chorus

all. _____ Grace it seems is all He has, and

one big op - en heart; And it's so good _____ be-ing

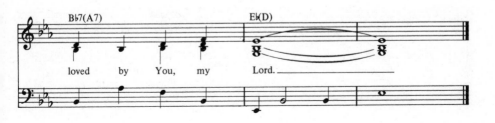

loved by You, my Lord. _____

2. We will know and understand
His purposes more clearly,
O, the mystery of the things He does
In making us more whole.
With His love He woos us,
By His grace He sets us free;
We can only trust Him
And just hold on to His hand.

144.   We are never alone

A. Woodroffe

We ____ are nev-er a - lone, ____ God has giv - en us His fa - mi - ly. ____ We ____ are nev-er a - lone, ____ In God's fa - mi - ly ____ we have se - cu - ri - ty. ____

Verse

1. In the moun - tains _____ or in the val - leys, _____
When things go right, _____ When things go wrong, _____
It's good to know _____ We have God's fa - mi - ly, _____
_____ A fa - mi - ly where we know we be - long. _____

2. As we share and as we live,
    As we receive and as we give,
    We will build up
    Each other till we all attain
    The fulness of the stature of Christ.

145.

We dwell in the courts
(He alone)

C. White

1. We dwell in the courts of the— Most High; We shel-ter in the shade of His wings.— He is our place of safe-ty; We— are se-cure in His pro-mi-ses. He a-lone— is my re-fuge, He's my God and I'm trust-ing Him.— The des-truc-tion

that stalks the dark-ness, Of this I am no long-er a-fraid. __

He a-lone __ is my re - fuge, I am no long-er a-fraid. __

2. A thousand may fall at our right hand;
   We stand alone amidst disaster.
   Evil will not touch us;
   From all we will be delivered.

3. We have made the Lord our refuge,
   We have chosen Him for shelter.
   His angels keep us from falling,
   In His hands He bears us up.

4. Because you cleave to Me in love,
   I will deliver you.
   I will protect you
   Because you know My name.

5. When you call, I will answer.
   I will be with you in trouble;
   You will know your joy fulfilled
   And see My salvation.

146. We have come into this place
(We have come into His house)

Capo 3 (C)

Worshipfully

Bruce Ballinger

2. So forget about yourself and concentrate on Him and worship Him, (*repeat*)
So forget about yourself and concentrate on Him and worship Christ the Lord,
Worship Him, Christ the Lord.

3. He is all my righteousness, I stand complete in Him and worship Him, (*repeat*)
He is all my righteousness, I stand complete in Him and worship Christ the Lord,
Worship Him, Christ the Lord.

4. Let us lift up holy hands and magnify His Name and worship Him, (*repeat*)
Let us lift up holy hands and magnify His Name and worship Christ the Lord,
Worship Him, Christ the Lord.

147.

We'll sing a new song

Diane Fung

Triumphantly

We'll sing a new song ___ of glor-ious tri-umph, ___ For we see the gov-ern-ment of God in our lives.

lives. He is crowned God of the whole world, crowned King of cre-a-tion, Crowned ru-ling the na-tions now. ___

___ Yes He is crowned God of the whole world, crowned ___ King of Cre-a-tion, crowned ru-ling the na-tions now. ___

148. We love You Lord

P. Lawson-Johnston

149.   We magnify Your name, Lord

Pam Hansford

Capo 1 (C)

Slow and with feeling

We mag-ni-fy Your name, Lord, _ We wor-ship and a - dore You, For who You are, For what You've done a - mong Your peo-ple here. We o-pen up our lives to You, Lay down our minds and wills, We want You Lord to have Your way, For we de-light in You.

150.

We shall be as one

J. Parsons

1. We shall be as one, We shall be as one, He the Fa - ther of us all, We His cho - sen sons; And by His com - mand Take each oth - er's hand, Live our lives in u - ni - ty, We shall be as one.

2.　　We shall be as one,
　　　We shall be as one;
　　　And by this shall all men know
　　　Of the work He has done.
　　　Love will take us on
　　　Through His precious Son;
　　　Love of Him who first loved us
　　　We shall be as one.

151.

We will sing praises

Capo 4 (C)

With pace and swing

Paul Armstrong

Lyrics:
We will sing prais-es to the Lord,— we will sing
prais-es to the Lord,— we will praise and ex-tol the Name of our
God.— We will shout glo-ry to the Lord, — We will shout
glo-ry to the Lord,— we will mag-ni-fy the Name of the Lord our
God. God.

152.   We worship Thee

T. Humphries

With simplicity

We wor - ship Thee Lord, On bend - ed knee Lord, Lord God we fall at Thy feet. Thy glo - ry flames round Thee, Thy saints all sur - round Thee and look to Thy mer - cy seat.

last time seat, And look to Thy mer - cy seat.

153. When I feel the touch

Keri Jones/Dave Matthews

Worshipfully

When I feel the touch ___ of Your hand up-on my life, ___ it caus-es
me to sing a song that I love You, Lord.
So from deep with - in ___ my spi-rit sing - eth un - to Thee, ___ You are my
King, You are my God, and I love You, Lord.

154. Why should I lose my first love?

1. Why should I lose my first love, When He's been so grac-ious unto me? He's dis-posed to for-give all the sins in my life,

They just melt at the whis-per of His word.

Chorus

O the na - ture of that smile on His for-giv-ing

face, _____ So warm un - to me When I

need - ed so much grace. _____ 3. I

2. Why should I lose my first love
   When I've seen Him so full of grace and truth?
   Why run away from that blessed ground
   Where I first met a love so warm and deep?

3. I love Him more now after I've sinned
   For I've found out what He is really like.
   He's a God of such love, He'll forgive and forget
   So I can put my full trust in Him now.

155.

Within the veil

Ruth Dryden

Gently

156. Wonderful Counsellor

Capo 4 (C)

Paul Armstrong

157. Worthy art Thou

D. Richards

Wor-thy art Thou — O Lord — our God — of ho-nour and power, —

For You are reign - ing now — on high, Ha-lle-lu-

jah. — Je - sus is Lord — of all — the

earth, Ha-lle-lu - jah, — Ha-lle-lu-

jah, — Ha-lle-lu - jah.

158. You are the King of Glory
(Hosanna to the Son of David)

M. Ford

You are the King of Glo-ry, You are the Prince of Peace, You are the Lord of heav'n and earth, You're the Son of righteousness. An-gels bow down be-fore You, Wor-ship and a-dore, for You have the words of e-ter-nal life,—You are Je-sus Christ the Lord.—— Ho-san-na to the Son of Da-vid!—— Ho-san-na to the King of—— kings! Glo-ry in the high-est hea-ven, for Je-sus the Mes-si-ah reigns.

159.   You have won my heart

Martin Alley/Ruth Alley

With warmth and simplicity

2. You shall have my love,
   You shall have my love,
   You have satisfied my soul,
   You shall have my love.

3. You're my heart's desire,
   You're my heart's desire,
   You have satisfied my soul,
   You're my heart's desire.

Index of titles and first lines

(First line where different from author's title is shown in *italics*)

Scripture index

KMR 315

KMC 315

'A Call to Christian Harmony'

For two decades a new light has been dawning through a fresh awareness of the Holy Spirit and His gifts. In the wake of this experience has come a deep longing for unity and a practical expression of the one body of Christ. Here is a musical embodying this desire.

Aids to Christian Harmony

LP — Cassette — Songbook — Music Director's Guide — Backing tape

All of these aids are available, except the Director's guide, from your usual supplier.

The Music Director's guide contains valuable information covering all aspects of presentation including details and prices of materials, putting together a choir and musicians, copyright guidance, narration and leading in worship. Full details of the mime, drama and dance items are also included.

The cost is £2.00 post free (in the UK) from:

Kingsway Music, Lottbridge Drove, Eastbourne, E. Sussex, Great Britain, BN23 6NT.

Kingsway

Kingsway Music present

SONGS OF FELLOWSHIP

As in the days of the psalmist when fresh experiences of the dealings of God led to new songs — so today new songs are being written as God continues to make Himself real to His people.

RECORDINGS

⊙ KMR 341 ▭ KMC 341
Songs of Fellowship Vol. 1

Sing unto the Lord a new song/We have come into this Place/Jesus is changing me/Our God reigns/Arise Arise/ We are being built into a temple/Abba Father/Jesus stand among us/Bind us Together/For I'm building a people of power & 10 others.

⊙ KMR 345 ▭ KMC 345
Songs of Fellowship Vol. 2

City O City/My life is really blest/ Jesus take me as I am/Come & Praise Him, Royal Priesthood/We shall be as one/Thank you Jesus/ Take my yoke/I will sing unto the Lord & 11 others.

⊙ KMR 358 ▭ KMC 358
Songs of Fellowship Vol. 3

Victory/You are the King of Glory/ Our eyes have seen the King/The Lord has built up Zion/O Lord you've done great things/We'll sing a new song/The kingdom of this world/ Within the veil/Ascribe to the Lord/ Lord God heavenly King/The Lord reigns/I will extol you/When I feel the touch/& others.

⊙ KMR 328 ▭ KMC 328
Draw near to God
Songs of Fellowship Vol. 4

Jesus, Jesus, Jesus/You shall go out with joy/We are a Kingdom/For we see Jesus/Sing to our God/I will rejoice/Promised land/Jesus name above all names/Rustling/Worthy art thou/My heart overflows/Jesus come closer now to me/I stand before the presence/I receive your love/Draw near to God.

⊙ KMR 329 ▭ KMC 329
Emmanuel
Songs of Fellowship Vol. 5

Great & Marvellous/O give thanks/ Halleluia, my father/Lion of Judah/ I delight to do thy will/Lord we want to thank you/My Lord, He is the fairest/River wash over me/Thank you Jesus/Where you go I will go/ Emmanuel/ & 4 others.

⊙ KMR 353 ▭ KMC 353
Songs of Fellowship Vol. 6

Jesus Jesus Jesus/Come to me/ I love you Lord/Jubilate Deo/Father we love you/I was once in darkness/Lord Jesus we enthrone Thee/Worthy, worthy, worthy/O the valleys shall ring/Let God arise/& others.

Available from Christian record stockists

Published by

Kingsway Music

Lottbridge Drove, Eastbourne, East Sussex BN23 6NT